THE BEST BITS OF Fred

Rupert Fawcett invented Fred ten years ago
and both their lives have taken off since then.
Rupert has got married and become a father while
Fred has become something of a star with books
and merchandise in several countries.

Fred's past life is documented in Rupert's nine
previous books: *Fred, More Fred, The Extraordinary
World of Fred, The Continued Adventures of Fred,
Carry on Fred, At Home with Fred, Pure Fred, The
One and Only Fred* and *The Little Book of Fred*.
Fred can also be seen in the *Mail on Sunday*.

The Best Bits of Fred contains 185 favourite
Fred illustrations depicting Fred's zany life with
the good–natured Penelope and ever–present
black cat, Anthony.

THE BEST BITS OF
Fred

Rupert Fawcett

HEADLINE

First published in 1999
by HEADLINE BOOK PUBLISHING

10 9 8 7 6 5 4 3 2 1

ISBN 0 7472 7420 7

Printed and bound in Italy by
Canale & C. S.p.A

HEADLINE BOOK PUBLISHING
A division of Hodder Headline PLC
338 Euston Road
London NW1 3BH

www.headline.co.uk
www.hodderheadline.com

FRED SPENT THE EVENING ADMIRING
HIS CORNFLAKE COLLECTION.

FRED SAT DOWN TO ENJOY
A SPOT OF LUNCH.

FRED'S QUICK REFLEXES SAVED
THE SAUSAGE ROLLS.

FRED FINALLY CONFESSED TO
EATING THE SOFA.

FRED AND PENELOPE PROVIDED
THEIR GUESTS WITH AFTER-
DINNER ENTERTAINMENT.

FRED SENSED THAT ALL WAS
NOT WELL WITH PIP.

THE EVENING WAS SPENT TESTING
PENELOPE'S NEW LABOUR-SAVING
LIPSTICK APPLICATOR.

FRED ASKED MR AND MRS NESBIT
TO LEAVE VIA THE SECRET TUNNEL.

THE BABY POLTERGEIST WAS BACK.

'SO THIS IS THE SIXTY-NINE POSITION,' SAID FRED GRIMLY.

FRED WROTE THE
SHOPPING LIST WITH
HIS NEW WATERPROOF PEN.

FRED ASKED CONSTANCE
AND PIP NOT TO WALK
ON THE NEW CARPET.

PENELOPE SENT FRED UPSTAIRS
FOR THE BIG TEAPOT.

FRED 'FLOSSED' HIS GUESTS
BETWEEN EACH COURSE.

FRED COULD FEEL A
NOVEL COMING ON.

FRED DIDN'T LIKE BIG
DISPLAYS OF EMOTION

FRED WAS DELIGHTED WITH HIS NEW
SWAMP-EFFECT CARPET

PIP LOOKED ALL SET TO WIN THE
DOG-OWNER LOOK-A-LIKE CONTEST

FRED LIKED NOTHING MORE THAN A
RELAXING AFTERNOON'S FISHING

FRED GREW ACCUSTOMED TO
PENELOPE'S TANTRUMS

FRED FOUND THE NEW COFFEE
TABLE SUSPICIOUSLY QUIET

'LAST WEEK IT WAS MARLON BRANDO, THIS WEEK MICHAEL CAINE', WHISPERED PENELOPE

PIP HAD DROPPED CRUMBS ON THE
CARPET ONCE TOO OFTEN

FRED COULD ALWAYS DEPEND ON
HIS IN-GROWING TOE NAIL TO
BREAK THE ICE AT PARTIES

FRED'S PRESENT CAME FROM HIS
FAVOURITE GENTLEMAN'S BOUTIQUE

FRED GAVE PIP DIRECTIONS
TO THE BATHROOM

PENELOPE HAD BECOME CONCERNED
ABOUT FRED SINCE HE LOST THE
KNOBBLY KNEES CONTEST

FRED LIKED TO KEEP ABREAST
OF CURRENT AFFAIRS

AFTER DINNER EVERYONE PLAYED
SPOT-THE-CAT

FRED AND PENELOPE OPTED FOR A
QUIET EVENING AT HOME WITH
THE CHAINSAWS

FRED WAS HOPELESS UNITED'S
MOST LOYAL SUPPORTER

'WE CALL IT 'TINA TURNER SYNDROME',' SAID THE DOCTOR GRAVELY

FRED WAS EXPERIENCING THE FAMOUS
'BOBBLE-HAT EFFECT'

PENELOPE CERTAINLY KNEW HOW
TO MAKE FRED FEEL SMALL

FRED INVITED HIS GUESTS
INTO THE BATHROOM TO
PLAY HUNT-THE-SOAP

PIP WAS BEGINNING TO WISH
HE'D NEVER MENTIONED
THE MOTH

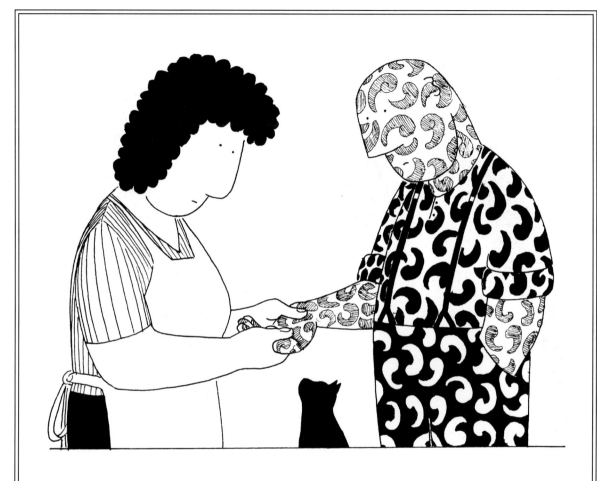

IT WAS ANOTHER OF FRED'S
PAISLEY ATTACKS

PENELOPE WONDERED IF BUNTY
MIGHT BENEFIT FROM A MORE
SUBTLE APPROACH

'ONE WINE GUM AND HE'S ANYBODY',
GROANED PENELOPE

AS USUAL THE MEN SPENT THE
EVENING TALKING BALLS

FRED WAS ALWAYS PLEASED
TO SEE THE NESBITS

AT TIMES THE TABLE FOOTBALL
COULD GET QUITE DIRTY

FRED SPENT THE AFTERNOON
JOB-HUNTING

PEOPLE CAME FROM FAR AND WIDE
FOR A GLIMPSE OF PENELOPE'S
DUST BALLS

'WHY DIDN'T YOU CALL ME SOONER?'
DEMANDED THE CHIN EXPERT

EVERYONE EAGERLY AWAITED A SLICE OF
PENELOPE'S UPSIDE-DOWN CAKE

FRED ALWAYS INSISTED ON
HELPING WITH THE GROCERIES

FRED THANKED BOB FOR THE
EXTRA PINT OF GOLD-TOP

PIP WAS BECOMING SUSPICIOUS
ABOUT FRED'S SO-CALLED
LUCKY STREAK

FRED LOVED TO CURL UP
WITH A GOOD BOOK

REAR OF THE YEAR

FRED ADORED COMPETITIONS

PIP'S APPLICATION TO JOIN THE GENTLEMEN'S ZIG-ZAG CLUB WAS REJECTED DUE TO 'INSUFFICIENT VISIBLE ZIG-ZAGS'

PIP HAD KNOWN THERE WOULD BE
A PRICE TO PAY FOR TAKING
FRED'S LAST HUMBUG

THE DENTAL FLOSS WAS
WELL AND TRULY STUCK

FRED OFTEN WONDERED WHY A GOOD-
LOOKING CHAP LIKE PENELOPES COUSIN
FRANK NEVER HAD ANY GIRLFRIENDS

FRED HAD BEEN WARNED ABOUT
LEAVING THE LAVATORY SEAT UP

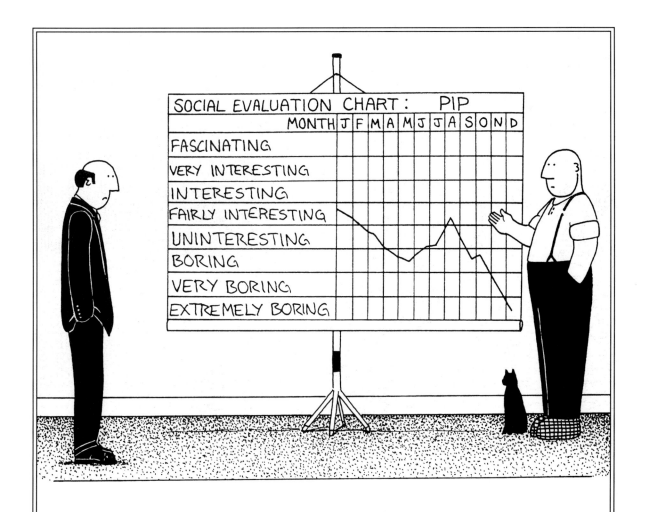

PIP HAD EVIDENTLY BECOME INCREASINGLY
BORING DURING THE COURSE OF THE YEAR

IT WAS TIME FOR FRED TO HEAR
ABOUT THE BIRDS AND THE BEES

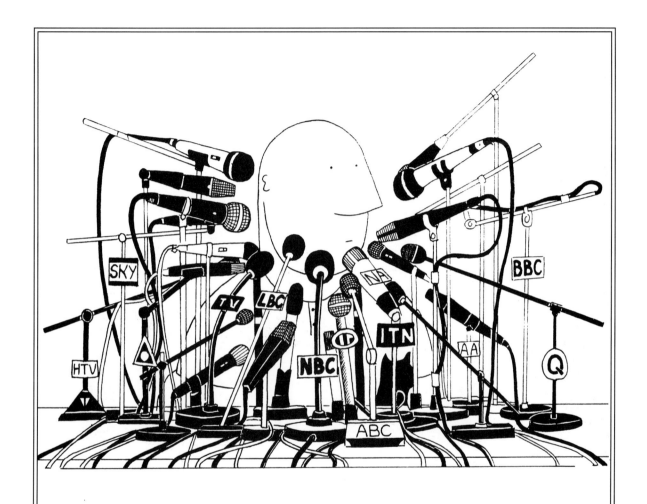

AFTER WEEKS OF RUMOUR AND SPECULATION
FRED FINALLY ANNOUNCED HIS DECISION
TO BUY A NEW PAIR OF PYJAMAS

FRED'S WAVE MACHINE TOOK THE
EFFORT OUT OF FAREWELLS

THIS IS WHERE FRED KEEPS HIS
STAGE-GEAR REVEALED PENELOPE

PIP WAS FINALLY INITIATED INTO THE
SECRET TOMATO KETCHUP CLUB

FRED AND PENELOPE WERE BEGINNING
TO WISH THEY'D NEVER HEARD THE NAME
'CHEEKY BATHROOM MIRRORS INCORPORATED'

CHIPPENDALES AUDITIONS
2.00 P.M. TODAY

FRED WAS DETERMINED TO PUT THE
YEARS OF UNEMPLOYMENT BEHIND HIM

PENELOPE HAD FOUND
HER VOCATION

FRED WAS ALWAYS REWARDED
FOR HELPING WITH THE GROCERIES

FRED HAD ALWAYS SUSPECTED THERE
WAS ANOTHER SIDE TO MRS NESBIT

IT WAS ANOTHER OF FRED'S
BOUNCY CASTLE DREAMS

PENELOPE'S DIET RESTRICTED HER TO
JUST ONE MINCE PIE OVER CHRISTMAS

FRED WAS INVITED TO SPEAK AT
THE ANNUAL DINNER-DANCE OF
THE ROYAL GUILD OF NOSEPICKERS

FRED SHOWED MR AND MRS NESBIT
TO THE GUEST ROOM

FRED WAS FAMOUS FOR HIS
CHRISTMAS BARBECUES

FRED ALWAYS LIKED TO GET
AWAY AT CHRISTMAS

FRED WAS READY FOR
THE CAROL SINGERS

'I GOT THIS ONE FOR WASHING THE
CAR AND MOWING THE LAWN IN
THE SAME DAY,' EXPLAINED FRED

FRED WISHED BOB WOULD JUST LEAVE IT ON THE STEP LIKE OTHER MILKMEN

THE BEST GLASSES ONLY CAME OUT
ON VERY SPECIAL OCCASIONS

FRED HAD NEVER BEEN
A MORNINGS PERSON

FRED HAD BECOME PARTICULARLY
FOND OF D.D.I.Y. — DON'T DO
IT YOURSELF

PENELOPE HATED TO BE DISTURBED
DURING HER FAVOURITE SOAP

'HE'S ALWAYS LIKE THIS FOR A FEW HOURS AFTER HIS OBEDIENCE CLASS, THEN IT'S BACK TO HIS OLD WAYS', SIGHED MR NESBIT

FRED SERVED COFFEE IN THE
TROPHY ROOM

FRED WAS INTRIGUED BY
PENELOPE'S LATEST HOBBY

FRED SPENT THE EVENING WORKING
OUT HOW MUCH MONEY HE HAD SAVED
BY DOING THE PLUMBING HIMSELF

PENELOPE WONDERED WHAT SORT
OF RESTAURANT FRED HAD IN MIND FOR
THEIR ROMANTIC VALENTINE DINNER

AS USUAL IT WAS 'STANDING
ROOM ONLY' FOR THE CHANGING
OF THE LIGHT-BULB

FRED SOMEHOW MANAGED TO GET
HIMSELF CAUGHT UP IN THE
WRONG DEMO

BUNTY ALWAYS SPENT HOURS
DRESSING FOR A PARTY

'FRED'S BEEN TALKING TO THEM AGAIN', SIGHED PENELOPE

THINGS HADN'T BEEN THE SAME
SINCE PENELOPE DID HER
ASSERTIVENESS TRAINING COURSE

FRED'S EVENING OF DANCE AND
MIME CLIMAXED WITH HIS MUCH
ACCLAIMED 'ANGLEPOISE LAMP'

BEFORE BEING ALLOWED INTO BED PENELOPE WAS ALWAYS REQUIRED TO SHOW SOME FORM OF IDENTIFICATION

'LOOKS LIKE TINY HAS FORGOTTEN
HIS GLOVES AGAIN', REMARKED FRED

'SHE'S HAVING ONE OF HER FAT AND
UGLY DAYS', REPORTED FRED

PENELOPE WONDERED HOW LONG
IT WOULD TAKE FRED TO NOTICE
HER NEW HAIRSTYLE

THE SPECIALLY TRAINED OFFICER SPENT
SEVERAL HOURS TRYING TO COAX PIP
DOWN FROM THE COFFEE TABLE

FRED WAS FORCED TO REMIND HIS LODGER
OF THE 'NO ELEPHANTS' CLAUSE IN THEIR
TENANCY AGREEMENT

FRED OFTEN WISHED PENELOPE
HADN'T INTRODUCED PIP TO HER
ASSERTIVENESS TRAINING CLASSES

'THAT'S HIS SEVENTEENTH ROLY-POLY STRIPPAGRAM THIS WEEK DOCTOR', FRETTED PENELOPE

'I CAN'T DO A THING WITH HIM',
SIGHED PENELOPE

NOBODY EVER SAID A WORD ABOUT
MRS NESBITS LITTLE PROBLEM

FRED AND PENELOPE SPENT ANOTHER
EVENING IN THE FAST LANE

WHERE PIP'S SOCKS WERE CONCERNED
THE KEY WORD WAS 'CAUTION'

AT LAST THE MAN ARRIVED
ABOUT THE DAMP

FRED'S LATEST INVENTION WAS DESIGNED
TO DO THE WORK OF TEN MEN

FRED FINALLY GOT LUCKY DOWN
AT THE JOB CENTRE

FROM TIME TO TIME FRED WOULD
TAKE THE MORE ADVENTUROUS
ROUTE TO THE NEWSAGENT

FRED AND PIP ALWAYS GREETED
EACH OTHER WITH THE SECRET
HANDSHAKE OF B.L.O.B.B. ; THE
BRITISH LEAGUE OF BALD BLOKES

FRED FOUND THE NEW WINDOW CLEANER
A LITTLE OVER-FAMILIAR

FRED HAD FALLEN OUT WITH
THE NEIGHBOURS AGAIN

AFTER TEA PENELOPE SAT DOWN
WITH HER KNITTING WHILE FRED
GOT ON WITH A SPOT OF D.I.Y.

FRED AND PENELOPE LOVED TO GET
OUT INTO THE COUNTRY AND
STRETCH THEIR LEGS

EVERYBODY WAS ASKED TO WAIT
PATIENTLY FOR THEIR TURN WITH
THE SCATTER CUSHIONS

FRED HAD PROMISED TO GET
MR AND MRS NESBIT HOME IN TIME
FOR THE ARCHERS

ALTHOUGH EVERYBODY LOVED FRED
THEY EACH HAD THEIR OWN
FAVOURITE BIT

IT LOOKED LIKE IT WAS GOING
TO BE 'ONE OF THOSE DAYS'

FRED AND PENELOPE HAD ALWAYS
SENSED THAT BOB WOULD HAVE
LIKED TO HAVE BEEN MORE
THAN JUST A MILKMAN

IF THE TRUTH BE KNOWN, FRED
WAS SICK TO DEATH OF PENELOPE'S
GARDEN FURNITURE BURGERS

WHEN FRED AND PENELOPE SET OUT
FOR THEIR MEETING WITH THE LOCAL
PLANNING OFFICER IT WAS WITH
A SENSE OF FOREBODING

PENELOPE WAS DISMAYED TO SEE
FRED FIGHTING WITH THE
NEXT-DOOR NEIGHBOUR AGAIN

FRED'S LIFE WAS ALWAYS
FULL OF DRAMA

IT WAS SAD BUT TRUE : VERA
REALLY DID HAVE A FACE LIKE
THE BACK OF A BUS

WHILE PENELOPE READ HER GLOSSIES
FRED GOT ON WITH A SPOT
OF GARDENING

PENELOPE FOUND THAT FRED'S NEW
MALE VIRILITY PILL HAD SOME
WORRYING SIDE EFFECTS

FRED WAS BEGINNING TO GET
FED UP WITH PENELOPE'S
VIRTUAL DINNERS

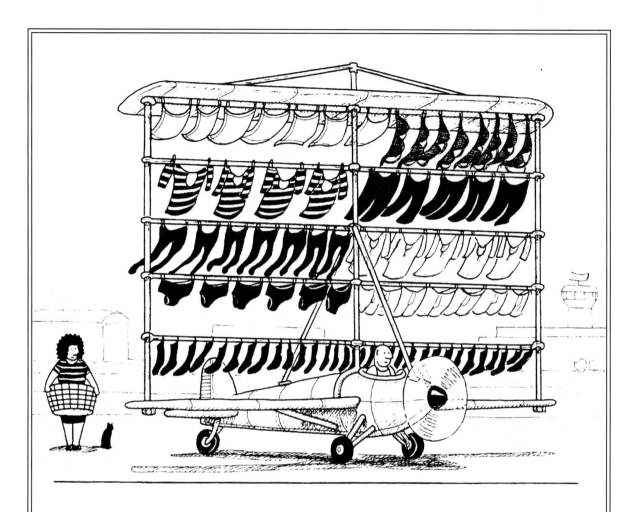

WHEN IT CAME TO DOING THE LAUNDRY
FRED AND PENELOPE MADE
AN EFFICIENT TEAM

APPARENTLY FRED AND THE BURGLAR
HAD BEEN AT SCHOOL TOGETHER

PENELOPE BEGAN EACH DAY WITH
A FEW MINUTES PRAYER AT
HER SHRINE TO GLADYS, THE
PATRON SAINT OF SHOPPING

PENELOPE SEEMED TO TAKE
AGES PUTTING ON HER FACE

'HE'S BEEN LIKE THIS EVER
SINCE HE LOST TINKY-WINKY',
WHISPERED PENELOPE

SUCH WAS THE POWER OF FRED'S
SUPERSTITIOUS BELIEFS THAT HE
REFUSED TO GO ANYWHERE WITHOUT
HIS 'LUCKY' WELSH PINE DRESSER

ANTHONY'S FRIENDS WERE
A CLASSY CROWD

THERE WAS ALWAYS A SMALL PRAYER
BEFORE THE OPENING OF THE
BANK STATEMENT

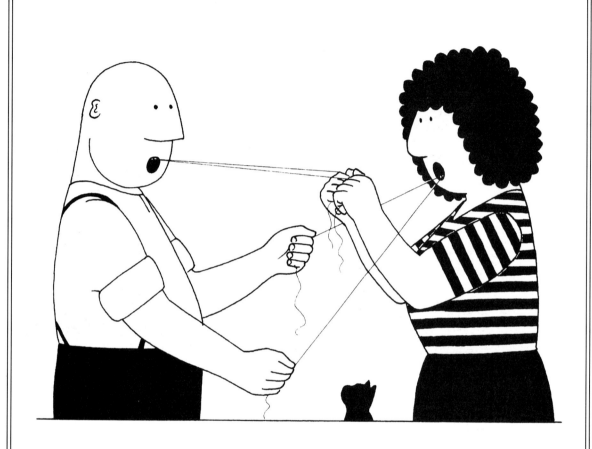

FRED AND PENELOPE LOOKED
FORWARD TO THEIR REGULAR
'FLOSSING' SESSIONS

IT WAS ANOTHER OF PENELOPE'S
TINA TURNER DREAMS

AS THEIR NEW LODGER UNPACKED HIS
BELONGINGS FRED AND PENELOPE
BECAME APPREHENSIVE

PENELOPE SOMETIMES WISHED FRED
COULD GET HIMSELF A NORMAL
HOBBY LIKE GOLF OR FISHING

IT WAS SO LONG SINCE FRED HAD
SEEN IT THAT PENELOPE VERY KINDLY
AGREED TO DESCRIBE IT TO HIM

FRED FOUND THAT BY USING AN
INFLATABLE REPLICA HE COULD
POP OUT TO THE PUB WITHOUT
PENELOPE NOTICING HE WAS GONE

BY TRAVELLING 'SUPER ECONOMY' FRED
AND PENELOPE WERE ABLE TO AFFORD
A LITTLE HOLIDAY ABROAD

SADLY, DUE TO LACK OF BUSINESS
ANOTHER FRED ENTERPRISE WAS
ABOUT TO GO 'BELLY UP'

PIP WAS BEGINNING TO WISH HE
HAD NEVER AGREED TO HELP
FRED LAUNCH HIS LATEST
BUSINESS VENTURE

FRED AND PENELOPE LOVED TO TAKE
OFF INTO THE COUNTRYSIDE ON
THEIR EXERCISE BIKES

IT TOOK A LOT TO DISTRACT
FRED FROM HIS NEWSPAPER

FRED HAD NEVER SHARED
PENELOPE'S ENTHUSIASM
FOR SHOPPING

PENELOPE HAD OFTEN HEARD IT SAID
THAT THE WAY TO A MAN'S HEART
WAS THROUGH HIS STOMACH

WHEN FRED HAD FINISHED HIS
IMPRESSIONS THE AUDIENCE
GAVE HIM A BIG HAND

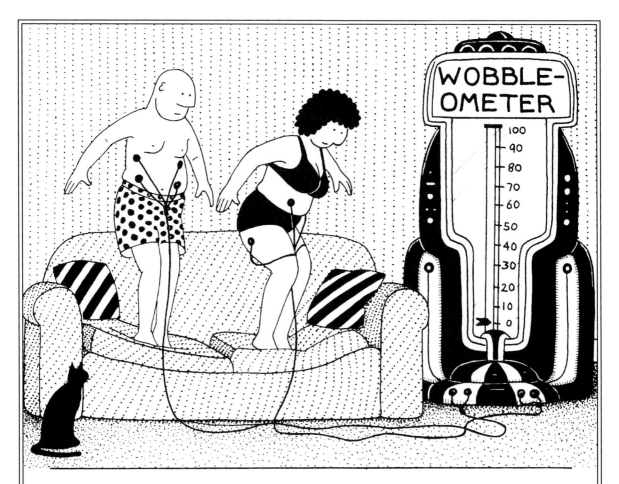

FRED AND PENELOPE FOUND THAT
BY JUMPING FROM THE SOFA THEY
COULD EASILY ACHIEVE A
MAXIMUM SCORE

PENELOPE SEEMED PREPARED
TO GO TO ANY LENGTHS TO
LOSE SOME WEIGHT

SADLY FOR JIM, THE WEARING OF A
TOUPÉE RESULTED IN HIS IMMEDIATE
EXPULSION FROM BLOBB: THE
BRITISH LEAGUE OF BALD BLOKES

FRED'S STRAP-ON CHAIRS ALLOWED HIS
GUESTS TO MOVE FROM THE LOUNGE
TO THE DINING TABLE WITHOUT HAVING
TO LEAVE THEIR SEATS

AFTER MONTHS OF UNEMPLOYMENT
FRED AND PENELOPE WERE FORCED
TO SELL THEIR HOUSE AND 'DOWNSIZE'

WHILE FRED WAS AT HIS DARTS PRACTICE
PENELOPE DECIDED TO TREAT HERSELF
TO AN INDIAN

JEREMY'S PREDICAMENT CLEARLY
ILLUSTRATED THE DANGER OF
STANDING CLOSE TO TREES FOR
LONG PERIODS OF TIME

FRED FINALLY DECIDED TO
REPORT THE STALKER

RELATIONS WITH THE NEIGHBOURS
SEEMED TO BE DETERIORATING

FRED PLANNED TO SPEND THE
MORNING TESTING HIS LATEST
INVENTION : A MOTOR CAR POWERED
ENTIRELY BY NATURAL GAS

FRED AND PENELOPE'S NEWSAGENT
CATERED TO ALL TASTES

'THIS IS THE LAST TIME WE
EMPLOY COWBOY BUILDERS',
RESOLVED FRED

IT WAS A CLASSIC CASE
OF LAWN RAGE

AFTER WEEKS OF NEGLECT FRED AND
PENELOPE'S BACK GARDEN HAD BECOME
A BIT OF A JUNGLE

PENELOPE OFTEN REQUIRED A
LITTLE EXTRA HELP WITH GETTING
UP IN THE MORNING

AFTER MONTHS OF WAITING, FRED
AND PENELOPE FINALLY RECEIVED
PLANNING PERMISSION FOR THEIR
NASAL EXTENSIONS

FRED AND PENELOPE DIDNT OFTEN
FIGHT BUT WHEN THEY DID IT WAS
USUALLY OVER THE LITTLE
THINGS IN LIFE

OVER THE YEARS FRED GOT
USED TO PENELOPE'S
VERBAL DIARRHOEA

ALTHOUGH PENELOPE HAD NO OBJECTION
TO GETTING OLDER SHE WAS NOT
HAPPY ABOUT THE CROW'S FEET

FRED AND PENELOPE
MADE A GREAT TEAM

FRED HAD BEEN LOOKING FORWARD TO
HIS BIRTHDAY PARTY FOR MONTHS

FRED AND PENELOPE WERE
DELIGHTED TO DISCOVER THAT
THE NEW NEXT-DOOR NEIGHBOURS
WERE THEIR KIND OF PEOPLE

FRED FELT HIS CHRISTMAS GUESTS
HAD OVERSTAYED THEIR WELCOME

FRED AND PENELOPE'S MARRIAGE WAS
GOING THROUGH ONE OF IT'S
DIFFICULT PHASES

WITH THE ASSISTANCE OF A FEW
FRIENDS FRED FINALLY UNVEILED HIS
LATEST LABOUR-SAVING CREATION,
THE SIX-HEADED HAMMER

MONDAY STARTED BADLY

'MY VERY OWN MILLENNIUM DOME',
SIGHED FRED

PENELOPE SO ENJOYED BACK-SEAT
DRIVING THAT SHE DECIDED TO HAVE
THE CAR SPECIALLY MODIFIED

PENELOPE COULDN'T HELP FEELING THAT
FRED'S ATTEMPT AT LANDSCAPE
GARDENING LACKED IMAGINATION

FRED ALWAYS MADE A BIT OF A DRAMA
OUT OF CARVING THE SUNDAY JOINT

PENELOPE INSISTED ON
EXTREMELY SAFE SEX

DURING TESTING OF HIS LATEST
INVENTION, THE 'WINTER DOGGY
SUIT' FRED REALISED IT HAD
ONE GLARING DESIGN FAULT

'AS SOON AS HE GETS BEHIND
THE WHEEL OF A CAR HE TURNS
INTO A COMPLETE ANIMAL',
SIGHED PENELOPE

FROM THE MOMENT HE WAS
BORN FRED SEEMED SOMEHOW
DIFFERENT FROM OTHER BABIES